Are You Coming Back?

David S. Watkins

Are You Coming Back?
Copyright © 2021 by David S. Watkins

First Edition

Hardcover ISBN: 978-1-63837-491-6
Paperback ISBN: 978-1-63837-492-3

The thoughts and feelings of Cat and Dog are their own, but you may have thoughts and feelings like them. Your thoughts and feelings are always okay. You can talk about your thoughts and feelings whenever you feel like it. Sometimes you may not want to talk about what you think and how you feel, but it can still make you feel better when you don't feel good. You can also look for your own special, warm place where you feel safe and loved.

Dog liked it when she looked into Dog's eyes and smiled. Dog smiled back. Her hands felt good when he was petted. Dog's eyes half closed. Yet, Dog felt afraid. Usually when she stopped petting him, this meant that she went away. That made dog afraid. He did not feel good. Would she ever come back?

Cat sat on the ledge, looked out the window, and pretended not to care.

When she walked over, Cat jumped down and walked away. Cat knew she was going away. Cat did not want anyone to know that Cat was afraid, too - afraid that she would not come back.

She turned around and opened the front door.

Then she said, "I love you," walked out, and shut the door. There was no noise. The house was very quiet. Dog stared at the door, and a squeaky sound came out of Dog's mouth. That meant Dog was sad and afraid.

Cat looked away. Cat never made a noise unless something felt good, and this did not feel good. *Nobody can know how I feel,* thought Cat. Then Cat walked away.

The sun was shining through the window, and Dog walked over to the spot on the floor where it was warm. Dog walked around in a circle and then curled up on the warm rug. A sigh came out of Dog's mouth.

Cat was on the windowsill again.

I am worried too, thought Cat, staring at Dog. *You don't look worried*, thought Dog. *I don't want anyone to know I am afraid*, thought Cat, staring at the warm rug, because nobody can help me.

Cat jumped down and looked at dog. Dog and Cat looked into each other's eyes. Just for a minute, Dog and Cat felt close together and stopped feeling alone and afraid.

Dog moved over to the warm spot to make extra room and looked at Cat. Cat stretched, very slowly walked over to Dog, and sat in the warm spot, too. It felt good to be warm. But there was not enough room for Cat to lie down with Dog, so Cat sat and sat and sat.

Dog did not mind that Cat was close. It would feel good to have a close friend.

Cat was getting tired of sitting. *Maybe I should lie down*, thought Cat. Dog smiled at Cat as if to say *it's Okay to lie down with me*. Then Cat lay down on top of furry Dog. They kept each other warm.

Cat and Dog did not know where this warm spot on the rug came from, but they felt Love in their hearts. They were glad that they shared their feelings. They weren't so different, after all. It was OK now.

Then the door opened and she came home. Dog's tail wagged. Cat looked up. She smiled at them together in the sunshine. The family was together again.

About the Author:

David lives in Laguna Beach, California with his wife Mary and Blackjack the cat that adopted him and the memory of his mixed-lab Bogart. He has written one other book, *How To Hit Your Second Shot First,* a primer for the sub-optimal golfer. He was inspired to write this children's book after observing the increasingly hectic lifestyles of those who must balance work and home that impact the young children who do not yet have a voice.

Lightning Source UK Ltd.
Milton Keynes UK
UKHW050344140722
405803UK00005B/203